Cooking Up Memories

from you to me®

JOURNALS™
of a LIFETIME

made with love *from you to me*

www.JournalsOfALifetime.com

Cooking Up Memories

from you to me®

This journal is for the favourite recipes and food anecdotes of your family or friends.

It is to capture some of those wonderful dishes or drinks that they have made for you and others over the years.

Ask them to complete it carefully and, if they want to, add some photographs or images to personalise it more.

When it is finished and returned to you, this will be a record of an amazing collection of recipes and stories that you will treasure forever.

Dear

Here is a gift from me to you . . . for you to give to me.

Food can produce powerful memories and I can clearly remember some of the wonderful things you have made over the years.

Please capture some of them in here along with your answers to my questions about your life with food and then give the book back to me.

I have listed some of the things you have made and I would really like the recipe for these, as well as your other favourites.

People say that we all have at least one book in us, and this will be yours.

The story of some of our favourite foods that I will treasure forever.

Thank you,

with love

"*After a good dinner, one can forgive anybody, even one's own relatives.*"

Oscar Wilde

These are some of the wonderful things
I remember you making. Please will you include the
recipe for these within this collection as well as
others you think I will like . . .

What are your earliest memories of your time in the kitchen?

Where does your interest in cooking and food come from?

Tell me the story of how you **learned to cook**...

What were some of your favourite childhood foods?

What were the **first dishes** you remember making?

Sweet shops bring back great memories . . .
what would be some of your favourite sweets?

How has the food you eat changed throughout your lifetime?

What are some of the most unusual foods or drinks you have ever tasted?

What family traditions about food or meals can you tell me about?

Tell me some **fond memories** you have of family meals . . .

Describe what would make up your favourite meal . . .

What are your favourite drinks?

Tell me about your Christmas dinners...

Describe your most memorable meal or meals . . .

Tell me about the best restaurants you have experienced . . .

Who has influenced you most with regard to food and cooking?

And who would be your favourite chef?

What are the **essentials** that you recommend I always keep in my **food cupboard?**

What books, programmes or websites
on cooking would you recommend?

What are your culinary 'top-tips'?

Tell me about some of the cooking tools or gadgets you have used or invented . . .

Tell me about your **funniest** cooking memories . . .

Tell me about your **most disastrous** cooking experience . . .

If you could **invite anyone** from the present day or from history to your **dinner party**, who would they be?

Describe your 'perfect day' when it comes to food . . . where would you have breakfast, what would you eat, what would you do for lunch?

What other **anecdotes** and **stories** can you tell me about your life with food?

With regard to food, what would you still like us to do together?

Favourite Recipes

Recipe name

Tell me the story behind this recipe . . .

Ingredients

Method

Recipe name

Tell me the story behind this recipe . . .

Ingredients

Method

Recipe name

Tell me the story behind this recipe . . .

Ingredients

Method

Recipe name

Tell me the story behind this recipe . . .

Ingredients

Method

Recipe name

Tell me the story behind this recipe . . .

Ingredients

Method

Recipe name

Tell me the story behind this recipe . . .

Ingredients

Method

Recipe name

Tell me the story behind this recipe . . .

Ingredients

Method

Recipe name

Tell me the story behind this recipe . . .

Ingredients

Method

Recipe name

Tell me the story behind this recipe . . .

Ingredients

Method

Recipe name

Tell me the story behind this recipe . . .

Ingredients

Method

Recipe name

Tell me the story behind this recipe . . .

Ingredients

Method

Recipe name

Tell me the story behind this recipe . . .

Ingredients

Method

Recipe name

Tell me the story behind this recipe . . .

Ingredients

Method

Recipe name

Tell me the story behind this recipe . . .

Ingredients

Method

Recipe name

Tell me the story behind this recipe . . .

Ingredients

Method

Recipe name

Tell me the story behind this recipe . . .

Ingredients

Method

Recipe name

Tell me the story behind this recipe . . .

Ingredients

Method

Recipe name

Tell me the story behind this recipe . . .

Ingredients

Method

Recipe name

Tell me the story behind this recipe . . .

Ingredients

Method

Recipe name

Tell me the story behind this recipe . . .

Ingredients

Method

Recipe name

Tell me the story behind this recipe . . .

Ingredients

Method

Recipe name

Tell me the story behind this recipe . . .

Ingredients

Method

Volume conversions

In most of the world, recipes use the metric system of litres and millilitres, grams and kilograms, and degrees Celsius.

The English speaking world frequently measures weight in pounds, with volume measures based on cooking utensils and pre-metric measures. The actual values are often different from the utensils on which they were based and there is little consistency from one country to another.

Measure	UK	Australia	USA
Teaspoon	5 ml	5 ml	4.93 ml
Dessertspoon	10 ml	–	–
Tablespoon	15 ml	20 ml	14.79 ml
Cup	285 ml	250 ml	236.59 ml
fl oz	28.41 ml	28.41 ml	29.57 ml
Pint	568.26 ml	568.26 ml	473.18 ml
Quart	1136.52 ml	1136.52 ml	946.35 ml
Gallon	4546.09 ml	4546.09 ml	3785.41 ml

Volume conversions

fluid ounces / pints	millilitres
1 fl oz	30 ml
2 fl oz	60 ml
3 fl oz	90 ml
5 fl oz (¼ pint)	150 ml
10 fl oz (½ pint)	290 ml
15 fl oz (¾ pint)	440 ml
1 pint	590 ml
1¼ pints	740 ml
1¾ pints	1 litre
2 pints	1.2 litres
2½ pints	1.5 litres
4 pints	2.4 litres

Measurement conversions

inches	millimetre / centimetres
⅛ inch	3 mm
¼ inch	5 mm
½ inch	1 cm
¾ inch	2 cm
1 inch	2.5 cm
1¼ inches	3 cm
1½ inches	4 cm
1¾ inches	4.5 cm
2 inches	5 cm
2½ inches	6 cm
3 inches	7.5 cm
3½ inches	9 cm
4 inches	10 cm

Measurement conversions

inches	millimetre / centimetres
5 inches	13 cm
5¼ inches	13.5 cm
6 inches	15 cm
6½ inches	16 cm
7 inches	18 cm
7½ inches	19 cm
8 inches	20 cm
9 inches	23 cm
9½ inches	24 cm
10 inches	25 cm
11 inches	28 cm
12 inches	30 cm

To be exact: 1 inch = 25.4 mm

Weight conversions

ounces / pounds	grams / kilograms
½ oz	10 g
¾ oz	20 g
1 oz	25 g
1½ oz	40 g
2 oz	50 g
2½ oz	60 g
3 oz	75 g
4 oz	110 g
4½ oz	125 g
5 oz	150 g
6 oz	175g

Weight conversions

ounces / pounds	grams / kilograms
7 oz	200 g
8 oz	225 g
9 oz	250 g
10 oz	275 g
12 oz	350 g
1 lb	450 g
1½ lb	700 g
2 lb	900 g
3 lb	1.3 kg
5 lb	2 kg

To be exact: 1 oz = 28.3495 g

Cooking temperature conversions

Gas Mark	Fahrenheit	Centigrade	Aga Setting
¼	225°F	110°C	Very Cool
½	250°F	120°C	Very Cool
1	275°F	135°C	Very Cool
2	300°F	150°C	Cool
3	325°F	165°C	Warm
4	350°F	180°C	Warm
5	375°F	190°C	Medium
6	400°F	200°C	Medium / High
7	425°F	220°C	Medium / High
8	450°F	230°C	High
9	475°F	250°C	Very High

For fan ovens, reduce recipe temperature by 20°

To be exact: $°C = (°F - 32) \ x^5/_9)$ and $°F = (°C \ x^9/_5) + 32$

Eggs

Description	Weight	Size
XL Very Large	73 g & over	0, 1
L Large	63 g to 72 g	1, 2, 3
M Medium	53 g to 62 g	3, 4, 5
S Small	under 53 g	5, 6, 7

Eggs are a perishable food and fresh eggs in their shell will keep for around 3 to 4 weeks.

Hard boiled eggs will last around 1 week.

To see how old an uncooked egg is, drop it gently into a bowl of cold water.
If it:

- sinks to the bottom and stays there, it is about 3 to 6 days old

- sinks but floats at an angle, it's more than a week old

- sinks, but stands on end, it is about two weeks old

- floats, it is too old and should be discarded

These extra pages are for us to write any food

questions, memories or answers that

may not have been covered elsewhere in the journal . . .

And finally for the record . . .

what is your full name ?

what is your date of birth ?

what was the date when you completed
this journal for me ?

Dear

I will treasure this book, your recipes and your memories forever.

I hope you enjoyed completing this book and answering my questions.

Thank you so much for doing it and for writing your own book about you and your food . . .

from you to me

Published by from you to me ltd

Share the things that really matter … share your stories with our website community at www.JournalsOfALifetime.com where journals can also be personalised.

Dear Mum
Dear Dad
Dear Grandma
Dear Grandad
Dear Sister
Dear Brother
Dear Daughter
Dear Son
Dear Friend

Cooking up Memories
Digging up Memories
Kicking off Memories
Drumming up Memories
Dear Future Me
These were the Days
Christmas Present, Christmas Past

Love Stories, anniversary & relationship journal

Bump to Birthday, pregnancy & first year journal
Our Story, for my daughter
Our Story, for my son

Mum to Mum, pass it on
Dear Baby, guest book
Early Years with Notes and Quotes

Mum & Me
Dad & Me
Grandma & Me
Grandad & Me

Rant & Rave, about My School
Rant & Rave, about My Holiday
Rant & Rave, about My Wild Life

Messages for you, on your special day
Messages for you, while you grow
Messages for you, while you're away

Cooking Up Memories

from you to me ®

First published in the UK by from you to me limited, September 2008.

Copyright, from you to me limited 2008

ISBN 978–1–907048–09–8

Designed and published in the UK.

Printed and bound in China by Imago. This paper is manufactured from pulp sourced from forests that are legally and sustainably managed.

For permission requests, contact the publisher at their head office address:

from you to me ltd
The Old Brewery
Newtown
Bradford on Avon
BA15 1NF, UK

hello@fromyoutome.com
www.fromyoutome.com